Universal
Saxophone
Edition

General
Editor:
John Harle

James Rae

20 Modern Studies
in Rhythm and Interpretation

20 Moderne Rhythmus
und interpretationsstudien

for Solo Saxophone
für Solo Saxophon

Grades 3–8

UNIVERSAL EDITION

CONTENTS/INHALT

PREFACE

This book has been written to familiarise the saxophonist with the various rhythms and phrasing encountered in modern music.

Each study deals with a particular aspect of rhythmic playing ranging from Jazz, Rock and Funk to Contemporary Classical. They are of moderate length in order to maximise concentration on style and interpretation.

The studies have been compiled in order of difficulty to enable the player to gauge his or her progress.

VORWORT

Dieses Album wurde geschrieben, um den Saxophonisten mit den verschiedenen Rhythmen und Phrasierungsarten der modernen Musik vertraut zu machen.

Jede Studie beschäftigt sich mit einem Teilaspekt des rhythmischen Spiels, das vom Jazz, Rock und Funk bis zur zeitgenössischen Klassik reicht. Die Stücke sind kurzweilig, um es zu ermöglichen, die Konzentration auf Stil und Spielweise zu erhöhen.

Die Studien sind nach dem Schwierigkeitsgrad geordnet, damit der Spieler seinen Fortschritt besser verfolgen kann.

James Rae

20 MODERN STUDIES
MODERNE STUDIEN

1 Turn about
Anders 'rum

JAMES RAE

10.9

2 Walk about
Immer unterwegs

3 Groove it!
Steig ein!

4 All change
Wechselgeld

5 Slavonic Dance
Slawischer Tanz

6 Heatwave
Hitzewelle

7 Helix
Wendeltreppe

8 Ambiguity
Zweideutigkeit

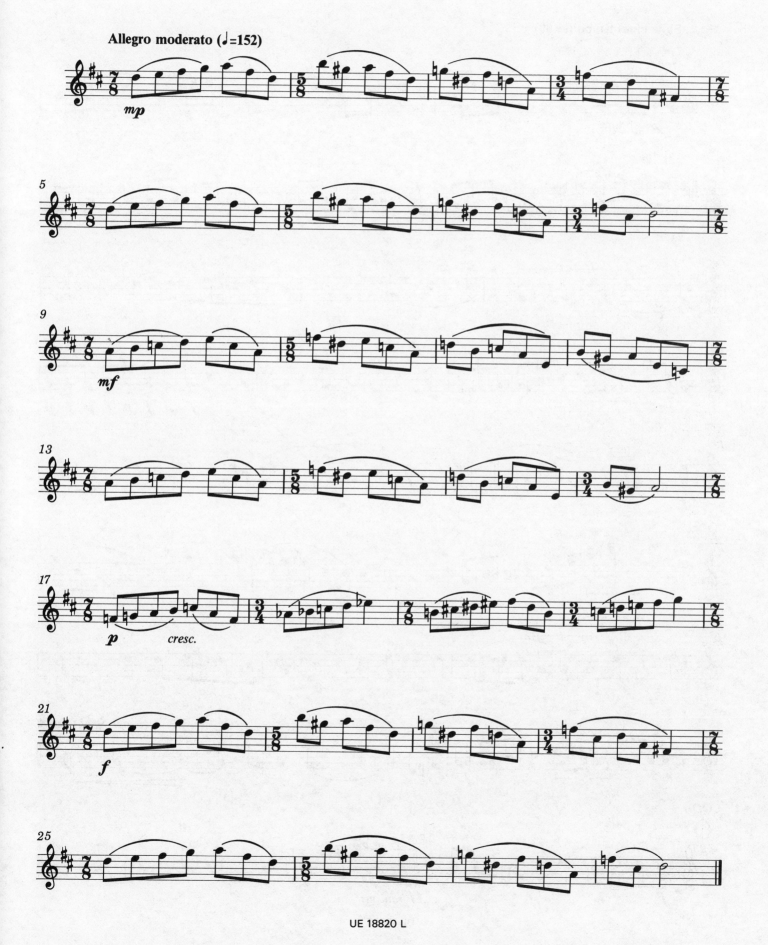

9 Soho
Soho

10 Latin Jive
Lateinamerikanischer Jive

17.9.08

12 Round and Round
Rundum herum

START
8110

13 Slurp, slurp!
Schlürf, schlürf!

14 **Hard Rock Blues**
Harter Rock Blues

15 'Dick's Licks'
'Dicks Leckerei'

UE 18820 L

16 Switchback
Drehschalter

17 'Snookie Dookie'
   'Schnuckiputzi'

18 **Inside-out**
Verkehrt

19 Side Winder
Schlingel

20 Cyclone
Wirbelwind

UE 18820 L

Reproduced and printed by
Halstan & Co. Ltd., Amersham, Bucks., England

Universal Saxophone Edition

UE 17770   **Easy Classical Studies / Leichte klassische Studien** (John Harle)

UE 17771   **Scales and Arpeggios, Part I / Tonleiterstudien, Teil I** (John Harle)

UE 17775   **Scales and Arpeggios, Part II / Tonleiterstudien, Teil II** (John Harle)

UE 17772   **Classical Album / Klassische Spielstücke** (John Harle)

UE 17780   **Bach J.S.** 2: Preludes and fugues BWV 857 and 885 for saxophone quartet (HUUCK)

UE 17774   **Bach, Johann Sebastian** Sonate G minor, BWV 1020, transcribed for saxophone and piano by John Harle

UE 17773   **Bennett, Richard Rodney:** Conversations / Zweigespräche für 2 Saxophone

UE 17447   **Berio, Luciano:** Sequenza IXb für Altsaxophon

UE 19071   **Viera J. Burghauser:** Balladen for 3 Saxophones (1 alto and 2 tenors or 2 altos and 1 tenor)

UE 17777   **Debussy-Album** for Alto Saxophone and Piano arranged by James Rae

UE 17778   **Gershwin, George:** 3 Preludes arranged for Saxophone Quartet by W Schlei

UE 13984   **Martin, Frank:** Ballade pour saxophone (cor de basset) et orchestre. Réduction pour saxophone et piano par John Lenehan

UE 17776   **Muldowney, Dominic:** . . . In a Hall of Mirrors . . . for Alto Saxophone and Piano

UE 19392   **Rae James:** Easy studies in Jazz and Rock

UE 18827   **Rae, James:** Jazzy Saxophone for Alto Saxophone and Piano

UE 18820   **Rae James:** 20 modern studies in rhythm and interpretation for Solo Saxophone

UE 18508   **Satie, Erik:** Album for Alto Saxophone and Piano arranged by James Rae

UE 17779   **Schlei, Wolfgang:** Invention for Saxophone Quartet

UE 18836   **"Take Ten"** for Alto Saxophone and Piano arranged by James Rae

UE 19075   **Vivaldi A.:** Concerto op. 3 / 6 (RV 356) arranged for E flat saxophone and piano by James Rae

UE 17575   **Weill, Kurt:** Music from the Threepenny Opera, arranged for Saxophone Quartet by John Harle

UE 17747   **Wildberger, Jacques:** Portrait pour saxophone alto en mi♭

This series will be continued / Die Reihe wird fortgesetzt

UNIVERSAL EDITION